My Little Orange Book

First steps in Bible reading

Pam Priestley

© Scripture Union 2004
First published 2004
ISBN 1 85999 717 1

Scripture Union, 207–209 Queensway, Bletchley, Milton Keynes, MK2 2EB, England
Email: info@scriptureunion.org.uk
Website: www.scriptureunion.org.uk

Scripture Union Australia
Locked Bag 2, Central Coast Business Centre, NSW 2252
Website: www.su.org.au

Scripture Union USA
P.O. Box 987, Valley Forge, PA 19482
Website: www.scriptureunion.org

The right of Pam Priestley to be identified as author of this work has been asserted by her in accordance with the Copyright, Designs and Patents Act 1988.

Scripture quotations are from the Contemporary English Version © American Bible Society 1991, 1992, 1995. Anglicisation © British & Foreign Bible Society 1996. Used with permission.

British Library Cataloguing in Publication Data.

A catalogue record of this book is available from the British Library.

Illustrations: Jenny Tulip at Beehive Illustration Agency
Cover and internal design: Mark Carpenter Design Consultants
Additional material: Maggie Barfield, Val Mullally (page 63)

Typesetting: Servis Filmsetting Ltd, Manchester
Printed and bound by Interprint Limited, Malta

Scripture Union is an international Christian charity working with churches in more than 130 countries providing resources to bring the good news about Jesus Christ to children, young people and families – and to encourage them to develop spiritually through the Bible and prayer.

As well as a network of volunteers, staff and associates who run holidays, church-based events and school Christian groups, Scripture Union produces a wide range of publications and supports those who use the resources through training programmes.

What's in this book?

How to use this book   4

Meet Jamie   5

Jamie looks into God's big book
The Bible   6–7

What's inside God's book today?
*God makes everything! Friends of God! How to live
God's way! Songs! Stories! Messages from God! All
about Jesus! Adventures! Letters! Wonderful words!*   8–29

Jamie discovers all creatures great and small
*Wild animals; Farm animals; Caring for animals;
Working animals; All God's creatures*   30–38

Jamie finds out about friends of God
Joseph; Moses; Jonah; Jeremiah; Nehemiah   39–49

Jamie enjoys stories of Jesus
Jesus goes to Peter's house; Jesus goes fishing;
*Jesus meets a rich man; Jesus at the Temple; Jesus
is very special*   50–62

Plus!

God makes everything   9
Make a scroll   20
Things to do with letters   26
Jesus on the donkey   36
Jonah and the big fish   46
More about *Tiddlywinks Little Books*   51
Fishing games   54
First steps in building self-esteem   63
More about *Tiddlywinks Big Books* for pre-school groups 64

How to use this book

When children are small, before they can read, it can be hard to know how to introduce the Bible to them. The *Tiddlywinks Little Books* offer a simple and enjoyable way to do so. Each book introduces Bible stories and truths through the lives of young children today. As they explore and discover and learn about the Bible in their day-to-day lives, they share their discoveries with us.

There isn't a "right" way to use *Tiddlywinks Little Books*. If you'd like to read something every day, each numbered page gives you a story and a prayer idea. Alternatively, you could read several pages in one go for a longer story. *Little Books* do not tie you to a certain date: use them as often as suits you and your child. Young children enjoy hearing stories again and again so don't feel you have to keep moving on or can only read a section once. There are extra pages too with ideas for activities, rhymes and crafts, and things for the children to do themselves. There is also a page for you, as you seek to introduce ideas about God and the words of the Bible to the children in your care.

You might like to set aside a time for using the *Little Books*, perhaps at bedtime or while you have a meal together. Or keep the book handy so you can use it anytime – on a bus journey, at a pause in a day of busy playing or while you're waiting for a visitor to call.

Children in their early years are growing faster and learning more than at any other time in their lives – an ideal time to take their "First steps in Bible reading".

At the bottom of each page you'll find a Bible reference. You can use this to show your child where the story comes in the Bible and to read the story yourself.

Meet Jamie

Jamie is four and has an older brother, Gareth, who's eight. They live with their mummy and see their daddy at weekends. Daddy has a new family now – Shirley and baby Jack. Jamie likes living with Mummy, but sometimes he wishes he could see Daddy more often, like Jack does.

When Jamie's mummy goes out to work, Jamie goes to a childminder called Sandra. Jamie sees his best friend Danny there. They have lots of fun together. Jamie loves machines, especially farm machines. His favourite toys are his tractor and combine harvester.

Mummy has a younger brother called Rob. Rob is 19 and works on a farm just outside the town. Rob often comes to see Jamie and his family on his day off. Sometimes Rob's dog, Harriet, comes too.

Rob has become one of God's friends. He has started to go to church and often plays his drums in the music group while everyone sings along. Rob likes Jamie and his family to go with him to church. Rob is really excited about God's big book, the Bible. He loves to tell Jamie what he has been reading from it. And Jamie loves to hear the stories Rob tells him.

I wonder what Jamie is going to find out next about the Bible…

"Hello! I'm Tiddly Tess!
Look for me as you share this book!"

Going to the library

Mummy was looking out of the window. "The library's here!" she called. "Rob, would you take Jamie and Gareth to change their library books, please?"

"Sure," agreed Rob. "C'mon you two!"

Jamie's library is in a big lorry! Once a week, it parks in the road near Jamie's house and the boys climb up the steps and go to see the books on the shelves inside.

Today, Gareth chose a storybook to borrow. Jamie found a book about tractors and how they worked. And another one about spaceships.

"I like coming to the library," said Jamie.

"Well, you have a library at home," replied Rob. "Do you remember that I gave you a Bible last Christmas? That's God's library. It has lots of different books in it. We could have a look when we get home."

"Yes, please!" agreed Jamie.

Pray

What is your favourite book? Tell God why you like it so much.

6

2 Timothy 3:14–17

A library in one book!

Jamie was in bed. Mummy went to kiss him good night.
"Mummy, look at my Bible," said Jamie, pointing to the book lying on the bed. "I've been looking at it with Rob. He says that it's his best book."

"Rob reads his Bible a lot," smiled Mummy.

"Rob says that it has lots of books inside it like the library-lorry," said Jamie.

Mummy opened the book. She showed him a page that said, in big black letters, "Genesis". "That's the first book," she explained.

Can you find the word "Genesis" in your Bible? It means "start". God starts to tell his stories there.

"I don't know the Bible as well as Rob does," said Mummy. "Perhaps we could look at it together. We could both find out more about God's story."

"Yes, please!" agreed Jamie.

Pray

Hello God. Thank you that I can find out more about you in the Bible. Help me to understand it.

2 Timothy 3:14–17

The first people

It was raining. Jamie wanted to play outside, but it was too wet.

"Come and play on the computer with me," said his big brother, Gareth. "I'll show you what to do."

Mummy heard them talking and laughing. She went to take them a drink and a biscuit.

"You see, it's nice for both of you to have a brother," laughed Mummy. "You've always got someone to play with."

God made one person called Adam. But Adam was lonely. There were lots of animals and birds in God's world but no other people. Adam didn't have a friend.

God said, "It isn't good for the man to live alone."

So God made a friend for Adam. She was called Eve. She helped him in his work. Later they had babies to look after. Adam and Eve and the babies were a family.

How many people are there in your family?

Pray

Dear God, thank you for giving me............ people to be in my family. Please look after them.

Genesis 2:4–25

God makes everything

Make God's wonderful world as colourful as you can!

Names for everything

What do you call a big animal with a long trunk for a nose?

What do you call an animal that purrs and has soft fur?

What do you call an animal that swims in the sea and has a hard shell on its back?

What do you call an animal that looks like a horse and has black and white stripes?

Did you enjoy guessing those? God gave Adam two lovely jobs to do. First, God asked him to choose names for all the birds and animals. That was fun. Then God asked Adam to look after the trees and flowers. Adam had to dig the soil. He had to make sure young plants had enough water. He had to pick the fruit from the trees.

Now we have tractors and combine harvesters and ploughs. They help us to look after the things that God made.

Elephant. Cat. Turtle. Zebra.

Pray

Next time you go out, play "I spy". How many birds or animals or machines can you "spy" (see)? Say "thank you" to God for each one.

Genesis 2:4–25

Abraham's big journey

Mummy was making tea. Jamie was busy looking at the

photograph album. "Mummy, look at Danny and me in the paddling pool," Jamie called. Mummy laughed, "Look at Gareth and his friends trying to do wheelies on their bikes."

"I suppose the Bible is a bit like a photograph album," Mummy went on. "It has lots of pictures of God's friends. Not photos, like this, but 'word' pictures that tell us what God's friends are like."

One of God's friends was a man called Abraham. Abraham always listened when God spoke to him. One day God told him to move to a new home. It was going to be a long way away. Abraham packed everything up and set off. He didn't know where he was going, but he was happy. Abraham knew God would show him where to go.

Pray

Dear God, help me to learn how to listen to you.

Promises

It was Saturday. Jamie was looking out to see if Dad was coming yet. Dad had promised to take Jamie and Gareth to "Splash time" at the swimming pool in town.

"Dad's here!" Jamie shouted to Gareth.

God made lots of promises to Abraham.

God promised to show Abraham where to live. Did he show him? Yes!

God promised that Abraham's family would be God's special people. Were they special to God? Yes!

God promised that Abraham and Sarah would have a baby.

Did they have one? Yes!

God promised that he would be Abraham's God and friend for ever. Was he? Yes!

And Dad didn't forget his promise to Jamie and Gareth! Can you remember what he promised them? Do you think they went to "Splash time"? Yes!

Pray

God has promised that he will always be with me. Is he always with me? YES!
(*Shout as loudly as you can!*)

Genesis 12

What to do

At church, everyone wanted to tell Jo their news. Reese, Lucy, Liam and Jamie were all talking and shouting at once. They were so noisy, Jo couldn't hear any of them properly.

"Shh," Jo said. "Sit down in a circle quietly. When I give you the teddy to hold, you can talk. Everyone will listen. Then someone else will hold the teddy. That's the rule. It's fair for everyone. We'll start with Liam."

God has rules for his people, too. One day God's people camped near a mountain. Moses climbed up the mountain. When he got to the top, God talked to him there. God told Moses he had written ten special rules for his people. The rules would help the people to know what was right. They would help the people to know what was wrong. They would help them to know how to look after each other.

Pray

Dear God, thank you that you gave us the special rules to help us to know what is right and good.

Exodus 20:1–17

God's special rules

Mummy and Jamie were walking to the Post Office. They saw someone running across the road, between the cars.

"That man's very silly, isn't he, Mummy?" said Jamie. "A car might bump him."

Moses knew that God's special rules were good. God loved his people. God didn't want them to get hurt. He didn't want them to be unhappy.

God wanted them to share. He didn't want them to snatch other people's things.

God wanted them to be kind to their mummies and daddies and families. He didn't want them to be rude and horrid.

God wanted them to tell the truth. He didn't want them to tell lies and get into trouble.

Can you think of a naughty thing that makes people unhappy?

Can you think of a good thing that makes people happy?

Pray

Here is a "sorry" prayer. You can use it anytime when you have done something naughty and you want to say "sorry".

Dear God, I am sorry that I...............
Please forgive me.

14

Exodus 20:1–17

Singing to God

It was Sunday. Mummy took Jamie and Gareth to the family service at church. Jamie wanted to sit at the front, near the music group. He liked to sit there. He liked to watch Rob play the drums. It was very loud. Jamie thought it was exciting.

Jamie liked it when everybody sang. He had a songbook too. Jamie couldn't read the words but he sang his own. Mummy said that they were singing lots of "thank yous" to God.

There are some "thank you" songs in the Bible. A king called Solomon built a beautiful new temple – a place where people could go and worship God. All the people gathered together to say "thank you" to God. They sang and prayed, "The Lord is good and his love never ends." Then some people played their trumpets very loudly.

Jamie would have liked to hear that!

Pray

Do you know a song about Jesus? Sing it for him now! Or make up your own song – Jesus loves to hear our singing!

2 Chronicles 7:1–10

Praising God

"Look at the picture I've done, Mummy," said Jamie. "It's a red lorry."

"Oh, Jamie, that's lovely. You've done it so carefully. I'll pin it up on the wall."

Jamie's mummy is "praising" him for his picture. She is telling him how well he has done his drawing and how much she loves him.

The "thank you" songs in the Bible often say "Praise the Lord". That means that we are telling God how wonderful and clever he is. One song says that we can praise him with different instruments. Can you guess what they are?

1. Praise God with the
2. Praise God with the
3. Praise God with the
4. Praise God with the
5. Praise God with the
6. Praise God with the

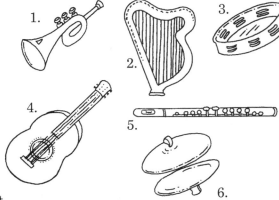

Play a praising game. Look at the pictures and pretend to play that instrument.

Pray

One, two, three – can you see? I am praising God today! With a bang, bang, shake, shake, rattle, rattle, blow – music that goes high and low!

Psalm 150

A soldier's story

Mummy was going to parents' night at Gareth's school. Rob came to look after the boys.

"Rob, could you put Jamie's eczema cream on before he goes to bed?" Mummy asked.

"Sure," replied Rob.

Rob smoothed the special cream on some sore places on Jamie's hands. "I've just been reading a great story in God's big book. It was about a soldier called Naaman," said Rob. "He had something wrong with his skin."

"Like me?" asked Jamie.

"No, his was called leprosy. There was no cream to make him better. No one could help him. A little girl lived in Naaman's house. She helped Naaman's wife. 'I know a man called Elisha,' said the girl. 'He is God's friend. Elisha could help Naaman get better'."

"Did he?" asked Jamie.

What do you think Rob said? Turn to the next page to find out!

Pray

Dear God, thank you that you know when we are ill and you can help us. Please help people who have waited a long time to get better.

2 Kings 5:1–14

Naaman has a bath!

Rob was telling Jamie the story of Naaman the soldier...

"Naaman went to Elisha's house. Elisha was God's friend. Elisha told Naaman how he could get better. Can you think what Elisha said, Jamie?" asked Rob.

"Have some medicine!" shouted Jamie.

Rob laughed, "I don't think Elisha had any medicine. He told Naaman to go and wash seven times in the River Jordan! Naaman was very cross. He thought the River Jordan was not a nice river. It would be like having a bath in a big, dirty puddle. Naaman didn't want to do that. But in the end he did do what Elisha said.

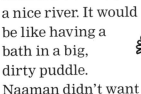

"Naaman walked to the river. He went under the water one... two... three... four... five... six... seven times. When he came out of the water, his skin was smooth and clear again."

Pray

What do you think Naaman asked God when he went down into the water? What would you like to ask God today?

2 Kings 5:1–14

A very important message

Jamie's mummy has a board hanging on the kitchen wall. It is made of cork. It has pins to stick in with red and blue tops. It is Mummy's message board. She pins on things she has to remember. Sometimes she lets Jamie stick the pins in for her.

One day God gave a message to his friend Jeremiah. Jeremiah's helper wrote it down for him, on a long piece of paper. It was called a scroll. Can you see the picture of it?
The message was given to the king. But the king did not

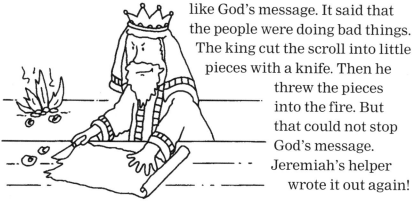

like God's message. It said that the people were doing bad things. The king cut the scroll into little pieces with a knife. Then he threw the pieces into the fire. But that could not stop God's message. Jeremiah's helper wrote it out again!

Pray

Dear God, thank you for your words in the Bible. Please help me to know what you are saying.

Jeremiah 36   19

Make a scroll

In Bible times, books were written on scrolls like this.

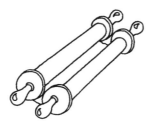
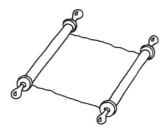

Here's how you can make your own scroll.

You will need: two cardboard tubes, a long strip of paper, sticky tape, pencils or crayons, or pictures and glue.

- Cut a long rectangle of paper.

- Tape each short side to a cardboard tube.

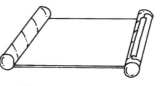

- Spread the paper out. Draw or stick some pictures along the paper, or do some writing.

- Roll the paper up from both ends, like a scroll from Bible times.

Doctor Luke's book

Jamie had to go and see the doctor. His hands were red and itchy.

"Mmm," said the doctor when she looked at his skin. "That looks sore. I think we'll try a new sort of special cream."

She wrote some words on a piece of paper. Jamie knew that they had to take the paper to the chemist. Then Jamie would get some eczema cream. That would make him better.

Luke was a doctor who lived a long time ago. He was a follower of Jesus. Luke wanted everyone to know about Jesus. He wanted everyone to be friends of Jesus. Luke tried to remember all the things that Jesus had done. Then he wrote them down in a book. Luke was pleased. Everyone could read about Jesus now!

See if you can find the book written by Doctor Luke in the Bible.

Pray

Hello God. Help my friends to know that Jesus can be their friend too.

Best friends

"Rob, is Jesus your best friend?" asked Jamie.

"Yes he is," replied Rob, with a smile.

"My best friend is Danny," said Jamie. Jamie was quiet for a minute. "But Rob," he asked, "you can't see Jesus – how can he be your friend?"

"You can't always see Danny, but he's still your friend," said Rob.

"Has Jesus got a red jumper, like Danny?" asked Jamie.

"I don't know that," laughed Rob, "but I do know that Jesus liked being with his friends. And he taught people about God. And he made ill people better. And he told good stories. I get to know lots of things about Jesus from the Bible."

"Did Jesus drive a tractor?" wondered Jamie.

"No," smiled Rob, "but he did tell a story about a farmer. I'll tell it to you one day…"

Pray

Dear God, thank you that Jesus wants to be my friend.

I want to be his friend too.

John 15:14–15

A big adventure

Jamie's brother Gareth was packing his rucksack. He was going to the school camp.

"Do you know what we're going to do tonight? We're going to light a fire when it's dark. Then we're going to cook sausages and potatoes on it. I can't wait," Gareth said excitedly.

"That will be an adventure," said Mummy, laughing.

In bed that night Jamie looked sad. "I want to have an adventure too," he said.

"Well, let's read an adventure story in your Bible," said Mummy. "Here's a really good one. It's about a man called Peter. One day Peter was locked up in prison. He hadn't done anything bad. He had just been telling people about his friend Jesus. During the night something very exciting happened. God helped Peter to get out of the prison. Peter couldn't wait to tell his friends!"

Pray

Hello God. Thank you that you're always with me wherever I am and whatever I'm doing.

Acts 12:4–11

Peter sees an angel

Jamie woke up early. He looked at Gareth's bed. It was empty. Jamie ran into Mummy's room.

"Mummy, Gareth's gone! He's not in bed!"

Mummy said sleepily, "Don't you remember? Gareth has gone away to the school camp. He'll be back tomorrow."

Jamie snuggled up with Mummy and she said, "I expect the soldiers in the prison were surprised when they found

that Jesus' friend Peter had gone! In the night an angel woke Peter up. The angel told Peter to get dressed. Peter and the angel went past the soldiers.

"They came to the main door. How were they going to open it? Suddenly, the door opened by itself. Peter and the angel walked outside. When Peter looked round, the angel had gone.

"Peter said, 'I know God sent his angel to rescue me.' Peter's friends were certain too!"

Pray

Dear God, thank you that you can always help us when something is difficult.

Acts 12:4–11

Paul writes a letter

"Mummy! Danny has given me a letter," shouted Jamie. He and Danny had been playing at Sandra's. Jamie opened the envelope and pulled out a piece of paper. It was covered in bright balloons. Mummy looked at it.

"Danny is having a birthday party on Friday," she read. "That will be fun. Would you like to go?"

Can you guess what Jamie said?

Jesus' friend Paul wrote a letter to his friend Philemon with some news. He wanted to tell Philemon about meeting a man called Onesimus. Paul knew that Onesimus had once worked for Philemon. Onesimus' name meant "useful", but he hadn't been very useful to Philemon. He had run away from his job!

I expect Philemon was very surprised to read in his letter that Paul had met Onesimus, wasn't he?

Pray

If you could write a letter to God, what would you tell him about?

Philemon

25

Things to do with letters

Post a letter to yourself!
Ask a grown-up for some paper to write or draw on, an envelope and a stamp. Make a letter for yourself! Go with a grown-up to post the letter. How long does it take to get back to you?

Out and about
When you're out on a walk, count how many letterboxes you see. Some are high, some are low, some are in doors, some are separate boxes, some are long, upright, shiny… How many different types can you spot?

At home
Where and when are letters delivered to your house? Do you get letters every day? Who gets the most letters in your house?

Stamp collecting
When people in your house have finished with their letters, ask for the stamps from the envelopes. Stick them into a scrapbook or on a poster. How many different pictures and colours can you find? Have you got any stamps from other countries?

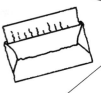

Be a postie
Make some letters for your toys. Put the letters in a bag and go round to your toys and deliver them. Why not invite them all to a dolls' tea party or a teddy bears' picnic?

Happy days
Send a letter to someone in your family who you don't see very often. You could make them a card or draw them a special picture to say "have a happy day today".

New friends

Jamie arrived at Danny's birthday party. He saw a girl who he did not know very well.

"Hello. I'm Danny's friend, Krista," said the girl.

"I know. And I'm Danny's friend, Jamie," smiled Jamie.

When it was teatime, Jamie and Krista sat together. They laughed at the funny hats. They threw balloons to each other.

When Mummy came to collect him, Jamie said, "This is Krista. She's Danny's friend. And now she's my friend, too."

Paul told Onesimus all about Jesus. Onesimus became Jesus' friend too. Paul told Philemon this in his letter. Onesimus and Philemon were both friends of Jesus now. Paul wanted them to be friends with each other. He wanted Onesimus to go back to his home with Philemon again.

Can you find Paul's letter to Philemon in the Bible? It is the smallest book in the whole Bible.

Pray

Who are your friends? Say "thank you" to God for them now!

"Thank you, God, for............"

Colossians 4:9

God's special place

Jamie had a special toy. It looked like a big tube with a little hole at one end. When Jamie looked down the hole he could see lots of colours – bright red, deep blue, golden yellow. When he pointed it towards the window, all the colours shone and mixed together as they moved about. Jamie thought it was very beautiful.

Do you know what the special toy was called?

At the very end of God's big book we can read about how beautiful heaven will be.

There will be bright jewels in lots of different colours.

The streets will look like pure gold.

There will be angels singing and playing trumpets.

There will be no darkness in heaven because God will be bright and shining like the sun.

And everyone who loves God will be there, with God, for ever.

Jamie's toy is called a "kaleidoscope".

Pray

Thank you, God, that heaven sounds so beautiful. Thank you that your friends will live with you there for ever.

Revelation 21

What's heaven like?

"I won't be able to come over on Tuesday because I'm going to Harry's funeral," said Rob to Mummy.

Jamie knew that Harry used to work on Rob's farm. Harry had helped Rob to get to know Jesus as his friend.

"What's a funeral?" Jamie asked.

"A funeral is a special time at church when we can say goodbye to someone who has died," explained Mummy. "Harry has been very poorly and he died a few days ago."

"So where is Harry now?" asked Jamie.

"He's in heaven," said Rob.

"What's heaven?" asked Jamie.

"Heaven is where God lives," replied Rob.

"Is it nice?" wondered Jamie.

"Heaven sounds brilliant," said Rob. "I've just been reading about it in the Bible. No one who is there will be sad anymore. No one will be ill anymore. And the best thing of all is that God and his friends will live there together always!"

Pray

Dear God, thank you for heaven. It sounds great. I want to come one day.

Revelation 21

29

Daniel talks to God

"Mummy, do you know that Danny's real name is Daniel?" said Jamie.

Mummy smiled, "I thought it might be."

She had just collected them both from Sandra's.

"There was a very brave man called Daniel in the Bible," Mummy explained. "He worked for the king. The king liked Daniel because Daniel worked harder than anyone else. Some of the other workers were angry that Daniel was the king's favourite. They decided to play a trick on Daniel and the king. These workers knew that Daniel loved God. Daniel talked to God, three times each day. So they asked the king to make a new rule. Anyone who talked and prayed to God would be put in a deep hole in the ground – with hungry lions! But Daniel wasn't frightened. He carried on talking to God."

Pray

Dear God, help me to love talking to you like Daniel did.

Daniel 6

Danny comes for tea

Danny had come to play and have tea at Jamie's house.
Whilst Mummy was getting the tea ready, she could hear a lot
of noise coming from Jamie's bedroom.

"Roar, roar! Roar, roar, roar!"

"Time for tea, boys!" Mummy called.

Jamie and Danny ran into the room.

"We're lions and we're going to eat you up!" shouted Jamie.

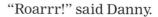

"Roarrr!" said Danny.

Mummy laughed, "The lions didn't do that to Daniel in the Bible. Daniel kept talking to God. So the king had him put in with the lions."

"Ouch!" gasped Jamie.

"No – it was all right," Mummy said. "Of course, everyone thought that the lions would eat Daniel. But they didn't. God kept the lions' mouths closed all night. God kept Daniel safe and well. Right," she added, "how about you two playing *sleeping* lions' and I'll put the sausages out?!"

Pray

What do you think Daniel prayed when he was with the lions?

Say, "Dear God, thank you for keeping me safe today."

Daniel 6

God is like a shepherd

Jamie, Mummy and Gareth had gone to see Rob at the farm where he worked. Jamie wanted Rob to take him to see the sheep. Jamie liked making "baaing" noises over the hedge. When they got to the field they heard a whistle not a "baa". Rob laughed. "That'll be Bill and Patch, his dog," he said. "Bill's whistle tells Patch what to do."

"Are the sheep frightened?" asked Jamie.

"No," said Rob, "they know that Patch is showing them where to go to get something to eat."

Soon they saw that Patch had gathered all the sheep together. Rob opened the gate for Bill, so the sheep could walk into the farmyard.

"That's what God does. He watches over us and shows us what to do. It's not just sheep who need looking after," said Rob. "We do too."

Pray

What is your favourite animal on a farm? Talk to God about it.

Psalm 23

Looking after sheep

"Can you show Jamie your crook, Bill?" said Rob.

Bill showed Jamie the stick he was holding. It had a curly end.

"Everyone who works with sheep has one of these,"
Rob said. "Sometimes a
sheep gets stuck in a
hedge. The
shepherd puts the
curly end round the
sheep's neck and
pulls him out.
David in the Bible
was only a boy,
younger than me.
David had the job of
looking after his father's sheep. Sometimes the wild animals
would try to hurt the sheep. David would use his stick and
push them away. He loved the sheep and wanted to keep them
safe."

Rob gave Jamie a hug. "You know, Jamie, I ask God each
day to look after you and keep you safe," he said.

Pray

Do you sometimes feel frightened? Ask
God to keep you safe.

1 Samuel 17:34–37

Meet Squeaky

Jamie was going to Sandra's. She opened the door.

"Hello Jamie," she said. "Come on in. We've got a surprise today in the other room."

Sandra showed Jamie a cage standing on a table. Inside Jamie could see a furry animal.

"I'm looking after a guinea pig," said Sandra. "She's called Squeaky."

Jamie loved watching Squeaky. He liked to see her nibbling at a piece of wood. He liked to hear her squeaks and the funny grunty noises she made. Most of all Jamie liked stroking her smooth fur when Sandra was holding her.

That night he told Mummy all about Squeaky.

"I hope she'll be all right on her own," he said.

"Don't worry," said Mummy, giving him a cuddle. "God is there with Squeaky, like he's here with you. God looks after little guinea pigs and big boys like you."

Pray

Thank you, God, for all pets. Help everyone to look after them properly.

Matthew 6:26

Jesus rides on a donkey

Mummy, Gareth and Jamie were going to the seaside for the day. They travelled on a coach. Jamie sat by a window.

"I can see lots of things," said Jamie.

"In Jesus' time people would have ridden on donkeys," said Mummy. "And, you know, when I was a little girl we used to have donkey rides on the beach. I loved doing that!"

Jamie couldn't decide which was better – a donkey or a coach.

One day Jesus had to travel to a big city called Jerusalem. His friends found a donkey for him to ride. Lots of people came to see Jesus ride past. They picked big leaves from the trees and put them on the road to make a carpet. The people knew Jesus was special and they shouted and cheered for him, "Hooray for God!"

Pray

Can you shout three cheers for God? Hip, hip, hooray! *Hip, hip, hooray!* HIP, HIP, HOORAY!

Mark 11:1–11

Jesus on the donkey

Jesus on a donkey comes riding in,
Riding in, riding in,
Jesus on a donkey comes riding in,
On Palm Sunday.

The donkey on the road goes clip, clop, clip,
Clip, clop, clip. Clip, clop, clip.
The donkey on the road goes clip, clop, clip,
On Palm Sunday.

The daddies on the road throw their coats on the ground,
Coats on the ground, coats on the ground,
The daddies on the road throw their coats on the ground,
On Palm Sunday.

The mummies on the road wave leaves in the air,
Leaves in the air, leaves in the air,
The mummies on the road wave leaves in the air,
On Palm Sunday.

The children on the road shout, "Hooray for the king,
Hooray for the king, hooray for the king."
The children on the road shout, "Hooray for the king,"
On Palm Sunday.

Make your own "palm branch" to wave

- Fold three sheets of newspaper in half. Roll up tightly and tape down the long edge.

- Make cuts from the top so that strips of paper hang down.

- Wave your "palm branch" as you sing this song to the tune of "The wheels on the bus".

The donkey's story

"My name is Barney the donkey. I was standing next to the road with my mum one day. Two men came up and started untying my rope. They started to pull me down the road. Someone asked them what they were doing.

'The Lord needs it,' they said.

"I was a bit frightened. Perhaps 'the Lord' was going to ride on my back? No one had ever done that before. It might hurt. Suddenly a man stood in front of me. He looked gentle and kind. I licked his hand. Was he 'the Lord'? Yes, he was! It was Jesus! I didn't mind when *he* rode on my back. I wasn't frightened when all the people shouted and waved palm branches. I was glad that I was the donkey who carried King Jesus. That's who the people said he was."

Pray

Think about a day you enjoyed. Tell God all about it.

Mark 11:1–11

Animal friends

Jamie likes
taking Harriet
for a walk
with Rob.
Harriet is
Rob's dog.
She is small with
bristly hair. Rob
sometimes
lets Jamie hold
her lead in the
park.

One day Harriet stood still. "Grrr, grrr," she growled.
Jamie saw a very big dog not far away from them.

Harriet started to run towards the dog, barking loudly. Rob
had to pull hard on the lead to stop Harriet chasing the dog.

"Rob, why doesn't Harriet like other animals?" Jamie
asked. "I thought Harriet would like to have some friends."

"You'd think so," agreed Rob. "But animals get cross with
each other, like people do, sometimes. They fight and scratch.
It says in the Bible that one day all the animals will be friends.
Wolves, lambs, lions and calves will be happy together in
God's kingdom."

Pray

Dear God, thank you for every animal
that you have made. You are so clever to
have made them all. My favourite animal
is.........

Isaiah 11:6–9

Little brothers!

Jamie and Daddy got the big box of bricks out. Baby Jack started crying. Daddy had to go and pick him up. Jack carried on crying. Daddy went to get a drink for him. Jack stopped crying. Daddy started building again with Jamie. Then, Jack started crying again. Silly Jack, Jamie thought. Silly baby. Jamie kicked the bricks box hard with his foot. The bricks fell out, all over the floor.

Joseph was the baby brother in his family. His brothers were cross when their daddy made Joseph a special coat. One day they saw that Joseph was on his own in the fields. The brothers wanted to get rid of him. They found some men who would take him a long way away to another country. Joseph's daddy thought a wild animal had killed Joseph. Joseph's daddy was very sad.

Pray

Daddy was doing things for Jack, but Jamie wanted Daddy to play with *him*. Have you ever felt like Jamie did? Talk to God about it.

Genesis 37

An important job

"Jack keeps crying," said Daddy. "I think his teeth are starting to grow."

Jamie felt a bit sorry for Jack. It wasn't very nice for Jack to be ill. Jamie picked up a squeaky toy and squeaked it at Jack. Jack stopped crying.

"Thanks, Jamie," said Dad. "You've done a good job!"

One day God gave Joseph a message for the king. Joseph told the king that for seven years they would have lots of food to eat. Then for seven years they would have none. What could they do? Joseph had a plan. They would save food in the first seven years so that they would have enough to eat in the second seven years. The king put Joseph in charge of storing food. He had a job to do. Joseph was very important now.

Pray

Ask God to help you when you have to do something that seems very difficult.

Dear God, please show me what to do when.........

Genesis 41:14–45

Brothers and friends

Jack smiled at Jamie. Jamie could see a new little pointed tooth in his gum. Jack put his arms out to Jamie. Jamie gave him a hug. Jack soon went to sleep.

"What shall we build then, Jamie?" said Dad.

Joseph did a good job of storing the food. The people had

enough to eat. But far away in their home, Joseph's father and his brothers had no food left. They were very hungry. Joseph's brothers came to buy some food. They met Joseph but they didn't know it was him.

Joseph wasn't little anymore. He had grown up.

Joseph gave them some food and said, "I am Joseph, your brother."

His brothers were afraid at first.

"Don't worry. I'm not going to hurt you," said Joseph. "God wanted me to come here. God knew that I would be able to look after you and save you all."

Pray

Think of children in the world who don't have much food. Ask God to help them.

The great escape

Jamie heard a "nee-naw, nee-naw" noise. He ran to the window. Three fire engines were zooming past.

"Where are they going?" Jamie asked Mummy.

"I don't know. I expect they're going to put out a fire. Perhaps someone is trapped."

God's special people were trapped in Egypt. The king made them work hard for him all day long. He wouldn't let them go. God sent Moses to rescue them. The people started to follow Moses out of Egypt. The king was angry. He would lose all his workers. He sent his army to chase God's people and bring them back.

By now Moses and the people had arrived at the Red Sea. The army was on one side of them. The sea was on the other. Do you think God helped them? Look at the next page to find out!

Pray

Whenever you hear a fire engine, you could say this prayer ...

"Dear God, help the firefighters to keep people safe."

Crossing the sea

Moses had a big problem. God had told him to rescue his people. But there was a sea in front of them. How could they get across that?

Here are a few ideas. Can you guess what they are?

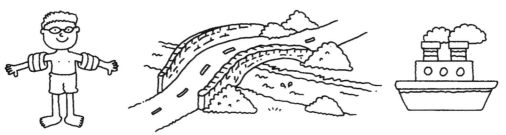

But not everybody could swim. There was no bridge. They had no boats.

God could solve the problem!

He made a strong wind blow across the sea. It blew the water back and made a path down the middle. Moses walked forwards. The people followed. Soon they were safely across. Then the sea came back over the pathway. The army of the king couldn't follow them. There was too much water. Moses and the people weren't trapped any more. They were glad that God had rescued them. They played music and danced. They were so happy!

Pray

Dear God, please help me when I need help.

Exodus 14   43

A job to do

Jamie was at Daddy's house for the day. He was cross. There was nothing to do. Gareth was at a birthday party. Daddy was outside. Shirley was busy with Jack.

"I've got a job for you," said Daddy, coming in from the garden.
"Put your coat on and come with me." Jamie didn't want to do a job or put his coat on. He did it very slowly.

Daddy was raking leaves in the garden. What do you think Jamie did?

God asked Jonah to go to a city called Nineveh. Jonah had to tell the people to stop doing bad things. Jonah thought to himself, "I don't want to go there and do God's job. I'm going somewhere else." Jonah got on a big ship and sailed away.

What do you think God did?

Pray

Sorry, God, when I don't do the things you want me to. Please show me what to do always.

Jonah goes to Nineveh

Grumpy Jamie slowly put *one* leaf in the wheelbarrow. Daddy looked at Jamie. He picked up some crispy leaves and threw them at Jamie! Jamie laughed. He grabbed some leaves to throw at Daddy but Daddy ran off. They chased round the garden, laughing, playing and throwing leaves everywhere!

"Right, let's get the job done," said Daddy. They both worked hard and filled the wheelbarrow.

Jonah wasn't going to do God's job. The sea was very rough. The ship went up and down. Jonah knew he should have done what God asked.

The only way to save the ship was for the sailors to throw Jonah into the sea! A big fish swallowed Jonah. Jonah prayed to God and the fish spat him out on to land. Jonah went to Nineveh. He did the job for God and God was pleased.

Pray

Can you think of anything you can do which makes God happy?
Ask him about it.

Jonah 2 and 3

Jonah and the big fish

When Jonah was in the sea, God sent a big fish to save him.
Draw the big fish around Jonah!

The fish took Jonah to a beach, where he was safe. Then
Jonah did what God had asked him to do.

Jeremiah in the mud

"I've had to give Jamie some of Danny's clothes to wear. His were so muddy," explained Danny's mum.

"What *have* you been doing?" asked Jamie's mummy.

"We've been sliding in the garden," replied Jamie and Danny. "It was muddy." They laughed.

There is a story in the Bible about a man who was put into some thick mud. But he wasn't playing, like Jamie and Danny.

Jeremiah was God's friend and he always said what God told him to say. But the king's friends didn't like what God said.

They put Jeremiah into a muddy well, so that they couldn't hear him speaking. Jeremiah had a good friend. His friend complained to the king. The king's soldiers pulled Jeremiah out. Jeremiah carried on speaking about what God told him to say.

Do you think Jeremiah's clothes were even muddier than Jamie's?

Pray

Think of one of your friends.

Say, "Dear God, help me to be a good friend to ...."

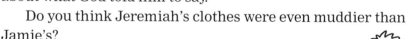

Jeremiah 38:1–13

Nehemiah the builder

Nehemiah lived a long way away from his home in Jerusalem. He heard that Jerusalem was in a mess. The walls were broken down. The wooden gates had been burnt. Nehemiah asked the king if he could go and mend them.
The king thought…

Nehemiah, can he build it? With God's help, yes he can!
The king said, "Yes."

Nehemiah went to Jerusalem. He was sad when he saw the broken walls. He told his friends that they must try and build the walls again. They thought…

Nehemiah, can he do it? With God's help, yes he can!

They said that they would help.

Nehemiah and his friends worked hard. They carried stones and piled them high. They rebuilt the walls.

Nehemiah, did he do it? With God's help, yes he DID!

Pray

Build a wall with your bricks. Remember Nehemiah. Keep shouting as you build, "I can do it. With God's help I can."

Marching on the walls

One Saturday afternoon Mummy took Gareth and Jamie into town. They found a place to stand on the pavement. Soon they heard the sound of a band. The band marched past them on the road. Gareth and Jamie laughed at the men playing the trumpets. Their cheeks were puffed out with blowing!

"It must be hard to march and play at the same time," said Gareth.

"It was even harder for Nehemiah and his friends in the Bible," Mummy said. "They had to march, play and try not to fall off the wall!"

When they had finished building the walls, the people wanted to say a very big "thank you" to God. The people marched on top of the new wide walls. They were so happy. Some sang and some blew trumpets as they went. They were so glad that God had helped them build the strong new walls.

Pray

Dear God, thank you for every way you help us.

Nehemiah 12:27–43   49

Granny gets better

Mummy put the phone down.

"I'm sorry, Jamie," she said. "Danny's mum says you won't be able to go to Danny's for tea tomorrow. Their granny is ill and they are going to visit her."

In bed that night Jamie asked Jesus to make Danny's granny better.

Two days later, the phone rang. It was Danny's mum saying, "Would Jamie like to come for tea tomorrow?"

"How's Granny?" asked Mummy.

"Much better, thank you. She's even baked a cake today."

There was a granny in the Bible who was ill. Her family asked Jesus for help. When Jesus went to see her he told the illness to go away. It did! Granny was better! She got up straightaway and went to make a meal for everyone.

Jesus made Danny's granny better too, thought Jamie.

Pray

Dear God, thank you for older people we know who are special to us. Help them to know that you love them.

Luke 4:38–39

First steps in Bible reading

The *Tiddlywinks* range of Little Books

My Little Red Book
First steps in Bible reading
Reese discovers Christmas is coming...
1 85999 659 0

My Little Yellow Book
First steps in Bible reading
Danny finds out about Easter.
1 85999 693 0

My Little Blue Book
First steps in Bible reading
Lucy and Liam find out All about me...
1 85999 660 4

My Little Green Book
First steps in Bible reading
Krista explores God's wonderful world
1 85999 696 5

My Little Purple Book
First steps in Bible reading
Lily discovers 'Jesus loves me'.
1 85999 720 1

My Little Orange Book
First steps in Bible reading
Jamie looks inside God's big book.
1 85999 717 1

Tiddlywinks Little Books are designed to be used at home by a parent/carer with an individual child. Linked to the themes covered in the *Tiddlywinks* Big Books, children can discover and learn about the Bible and share their discoveries with you. There are 50 first steps in Bible reading pages in each book, with a story for each day and extra activity pages of fun things to do. Children will love exploring the Bible with child characters Lucy and Liam, Reese, Danny, Krista, Lily and Jamie.
A5, 64pp £3.50 each (Prices subject to change)

You can order these or any other *Tiddlywinks* resources from:

- Your local Christian bookstore
- Scripture Union Mail Order: Telephone 01908 856006
- Online: log on to
  www.scriptureunion.org.uk/tiddlywinks
  to order securely from our online bookshop

66 *When the Big Books are used in conjunction with the Little Books, children and adults encounter an attractive mixture of stories and activities that will encourage everybody to know and trust in Jesus.* 99
Diana Turner,
Editor of Playleader Magazine

Tiddlywinks

The flexible resource for pre-school children and carers

Also now on sale!
Glitter and Glue. Pray and Play.
Even more craft and prayer ideas for use with under fives

Jesus teaches

"I'm too tired to cook tonight," said Mummy. "We'll go and buy fish and chips for tea."

"Did Jesus have chips with his fish?" asked Jamie. Mummy smiled.

"I don't think the Bible talks about chips. But I expect Jesus ate fish a lot. Many of his friends were fishermen."

One day Jesus was on the beach by a big lake, almost as big as the sea. Lots of people wanted to hear Jesus' stories. They were crowding round him. The people at the back couldn't see or hear very well. Jesus asked fisherman Peter if he could use his boat. Peter was glad to help Jesus. Peter rowed the boat a little way out. Jesus told stories from the boat. Everyone was pleased. They could all see and hear him now. They wanted to learn how to be Jesus' friends.

Pray

Dear God, thank you for all the lovely stories that Jesus told.

Luke 5:1–11

Fishing at night

Row, row, row your boat
Out onto the lake.
Let's see what
we can catch,
If we can stay
awake!

I wonder if
Jesus' friends
sang a song like
this when they
went fishing?

One night Peter and the other fishermen rowed out in their boats. They were excited. Night-time was a good time for catching fish. They lowered their nets over the side of the boat.

"Have you caught anything yet, Peter?" shouted John from the other boat. Peter pulled the net up.

"No," he replied.

"Me neither," said John. They started to feel sleepy.

"Got any fish?" called Peter a bit later.

"No," said John. They spent all night in their boats. They didn't catch one fish. No one felt like singing. But one of their friends could help them. Can you think who that might be?

Pray

Hello God! Please can you keep all fishermen safe when they are out at sea?

Luke 5:1–11

Fishing games

Catch a fish

Draw a few fish shapes on coloured paper and cut them out.

Clip a metal paper clip to each fish. Put all your fish in a bowl or box.

Make a fishing rod from a stick with a piece of string tied on. Fix a magnet to the other end of the string.

Hold the rod over the bowl and see how many fish you can catch.

Flap a fish

Make a fish from thin paper or tissue – you will need one fish for each person playing.

Put your fish on the floor.

Roll up an old newspaper. Hit this on the floor just behind your fish and watch the fish jump!

Who can make their fish move the farthest?

Full nets

Jamie often talks to Rob when he is sad about something.

"Danny's going away on holiday for two weeks. I won't have anyone to play with at Sandra's," said Jamie.

"Never mind," said Rob. "You'll have some great times when he comes back."

Peter the fisherman talked to his friend Jesus, "We've tried all night and haven't caught a single fish."

"Row out into the deep water and try again," said Jesus. Peter rowed out. After a little while Peter thought he would

check the nets. He pulled. The net would not come out of the water. He pulled again. The net would still not come. Peter looked down into the water. The net was full of hundreds of silver fish. Peter's friends had to help him to pull it out!

Peter knew then that Jesus was very special.

Pray

Tell Jesus about all the things you've done today.

Luke 5:1–11

Jesus meets a young man

"Jamie, put your fleecy jacket on. Daddy's picking you up soon," called Mummy.

"I'm eating my toast," said Jamie.

"Right, eat your toast, then put your fleece on," said Mummy.

"I want to wear just my T-shirt," replied Jamie.

"No. It's cold and you need your fleece," said Mummy.

"I don't want to put it on yet," said Jamie.

"If you don't put it on now, you'll be too cold to go outside with Daddy," replied Mummy.

One day a man went up to Jesus. He really wanted to know how to be Jesus' friend. Jesus told him about God's special rules, which helped people to look after each other.

"I have always looked after people," said the man. Jesus knew that he was a good man. Jesus liked the man. He was pleased the man wanted to be his friend.

Pray

Dear God, help me to find out more about being your friend.

Mark 10:17–31

The man and his money

Daddy and Jack had arrived to take Jamie to the park.

"I'm not wearing my silly fleece," shouted Jamie.

Mummy went outside. "Daddy is taking Jack on his own to the park," Mummy said as she came back in. Jamie burst into tears and stamped his foot.

"But I wanted to go," he cried.

Jesus knew that the man who had come to him really wanted to be his friend. Jesus told him that there was one thing he had to do.

"Give all your money away and then come and be my friend," said Jesus. The man had a lot of money and he didn't want to give it away. He thought his money was more important than being Jesus' friend. He walked away sadly. Jesus was sad too.

Pray

What do you find really hard to do? What don't you like doing? Talk to God about it.

Mark 10:17–31

Something for Jamie

"Jamie, let's pop in to see if Phyllis is all right," said Mummy.

Phyllis was an old lady who lived down the road.

Phyllis was very pleased to see them.

She made them both a drink. Before they left, she pushed something into Jamie's hand. It was a bright shiny coin.

"Oh Phyllis, you shouldn't," said Mummy.

"Go on with you. I like to give him something," replied Phyllis.

On the way home Mummy said, "Phyllis hasn't got very much money, but she always likes to give. One day Jesus saw rich people putting money into a collecting box. They still had lots of money left. A poor woman put in two little pennies. That was everything she had. She had no more money left. Jesus was pleased with her because she was happy to share everything she had."

Pray

Dear God, help me to share and not be mean.

Luke 21:1–4

Giving the best

"Someone at work is collecting toys for refugee children," said Mummy. "Have you two got anything that you can give?"

"What are refugees?" asked Gareth.

"Refugees are people who have had to leave their homes and all their things, and move to another country."

Jamie went into his bedroom. He looked around. Suddenly he saw his alphabet jigsaw. It had a piece missing. He didn't want that. He could give that.

Just then Jamie remembered the story from the Bible

about the woman who gave everything she had to God. Jamie picked up his tractor and trailer. It was one of his best toys. He took it downstairs.

"I want to give this," he said.

"But Jamie, that cost a lot of money."

"But they haven't got *any* toys," Jamie said.

Mummy was quiet, then she hugged Jamie. "They'll love that," she said.

Pray

Remember children who have had to leave their country, their home and their toys behind. Ask God to take care of them.

Luke 21:1–4

Jesus is alive

Jamie and Mummy were planting bulbs in a bowl. Jamie opened the bag to get them out.

"Ugh, Mummy these are horrid and dead. We'll have to buy some new ones."

"They don't look very nice," agreed Mummy. "But after they have slept in the soil all winter, they will have beautiful flowers."

One sad day, Jesus' friends saw him die. They knew that his body had been put in a cave. A big stone had been rolled in front of it. Some of Jesus' friends went to see the cave. When they got there they were shocked! Can you see their faces in the picture? The big stone had been rolled away! The cave was empty! And there was an angel!! The angel told them, "Jesus isn't here. God has made him alive again."

Pray

Thank you for the angel's news that Jesus is alive! I'm glad that he can be my friend.

Jesus is alive!

Jamie was helping Rob to move stones in the wheelbarrow. One was so big that they could hardly push it.

"Is that as big as the 'rollaway' stone?" asked Jamie.

"The what?" said Rob.

"The 'rollaway' stone. It rolled away and then Jesus could get out."

"Oh, *that* stone," said Rob, smiling. "I think that was bigger."

"What did Jesus do after he got out? Did he go home?" asked Jamie.

"The first thing he did was to talk to his friend Mary. She was very surprised. She thought that he was the gardener. Then he went to see some of his other friends. They were all very pleased to see him. They knew that they still had Jesus as their friend. And he would be their friend always."

"Is he your friend, Rob?"

"He is," said Rob.

"He's my friend too," said Jamie.

Pray

Shout three times, "Jesus is alive! He's my friend!"

Time to go

Shirley, Jack, Gareth and Jamie were at the airport. Daddy was going to America. They were saying goodbye to him. "I'll be back soon," Daddy said to Jamie. Daddy kissed them all and went through the door. They waited until Daddy's plane took off. When they couldn't see it anymore, they went back to the car. They felt a bit sad, but they knew they would see Daddy again soon.

Jesus told his friends that it was time to leave them. He wanted them to carry on telling everyone that he was their friend. Then he said  goodbye. At first they could see him but then he disappeared. His friends knew that he was at home with God, his father. They were happy because they knew that even though they could not see him, Jesus would be with them always.

Pray

Dear God, thank you that Jesus is at home with you. And he's with me too!

Acts 1:6–11

First steps in building self-esteem

Parents often fret: "Will my child go off the rails/take drugs/have an unwanted pregnancy?" – all legitimate concerns. And we don't *start* worrying about these matters when they're in their teens. We're already concerned about these "nightmares" when they're still toddling around in the sandpit! But that's good news – because we can make the most significant difference when we start at the earliest stages.

Our children deserve the same sensitive discipling that Jesus gave to his own early followers. Besides his unwavering personal example, his approach was one of building self-esteem. He came alongside his friends, helping them to learn to do things for themselves – and allowing them to make mistakes.

Even in small, everyday situations we have the opportunity to build a firm foundation for our children – a house on the rock, rather than on the sand.

Here are four corner stones for this:

- Point out even the smallest things that your child does successfully (eg saying, "You've tidied away all your toys – well done," is a far more helpful form of praise to a child than, "That's good.")
- Comment on positive character traits, such as helpfulness, kindness, etc.
- Involve your child so that they know they have something to contribute too.
- Affirm your child's sense of belonging by giving reassurance of your love, through kind actions as well as words.

Children sense our belief in them as competent, caring human beings, even as Jesus demonstrated his confidence in his first followers. When even the youngest children know that they are valued, then they are in a position of naturally having something to give back to the world. We can be part of building a generation of children with belief in themselves and the confidence to make a difference!

Have you enjoyed this book?

Then take a look at the Big Books in the *Tiddlywinks* range.
Why not try them all?

The Big Orange Book
Themes: What's inside God's big book? All creatures great and small; Friends of God; Stories of Jesus
1 85999 716 3

The Big Red Book
Themes: Christmas is coming; People we meet; Stories Jesus told; God gives us food
1 85999 658 2

The Big Blue Book
Themes: All about me; God gives us... homes, clothes, food, etc; People who knew Jesus; Friends of God
1 85999 657 4

The Big Yellow Book
Themes: Easter; God gives us families; Friends of Jesus; What's the weather like?
1 85999 692 2

The Big Green Book
Themes: God's wonderful world; God gives us people; Let's find out about Jesus; God knows when I'm... happy, cross, sad, scared, busy
1 85999 695 7

The Big Purple Book
Themes: Jesus loves me; God loves it when I... make music, sing, dance, look at books, I'm 'me'; Friends and followers; Materials and technology
1 85999 719 8

'I love this! It's great!' Sarah, leader of a 3 to 5s group in Victoria, Australia.

'...really pleased with your material and look forward to integrating Tiddlywinks into our existing programme.' Marion, Scotland

Tiddlywinks Big Books are designed for use in any pre-school setting. The multi-purpose outlines are packed full of play, prayers, crafts, stories and rhymes; simply pick and mix ideas to meet the particular needs of your group. You'll find plenty of practical advice on setting up and running a pre-school group, plus ideas in every session to help you include adult carers. The children will love the illustrated activity pages.
A4, 96pp, £8.99 each (Prices subject to change)

You can order these or any other *Tiddlywinks* resources from:

● Your local Christian bookstore
● Scripture Union Mail Order: Telephone 01908 856006
● Online: log on to **www.scriptureunion.org.uk/tiddlywinks** to order securely from our online bookshop

The flexible resource for pre-school children and carers

Also now on sale
Glitter and Glue. Pray and Play.
Even more craft and prayer ideas for use with under fives